Printed and Published by D. C. Thomson & Co., Ltd., 185 Fleet Street, London EC4A 2HS.

ISBN 0 85116 779 9

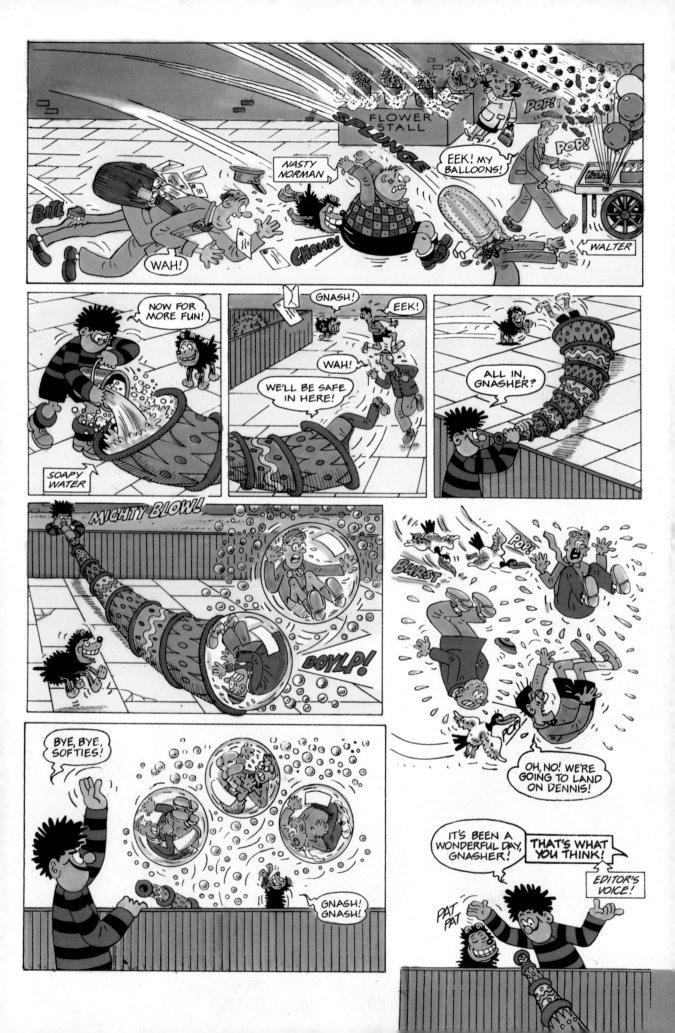

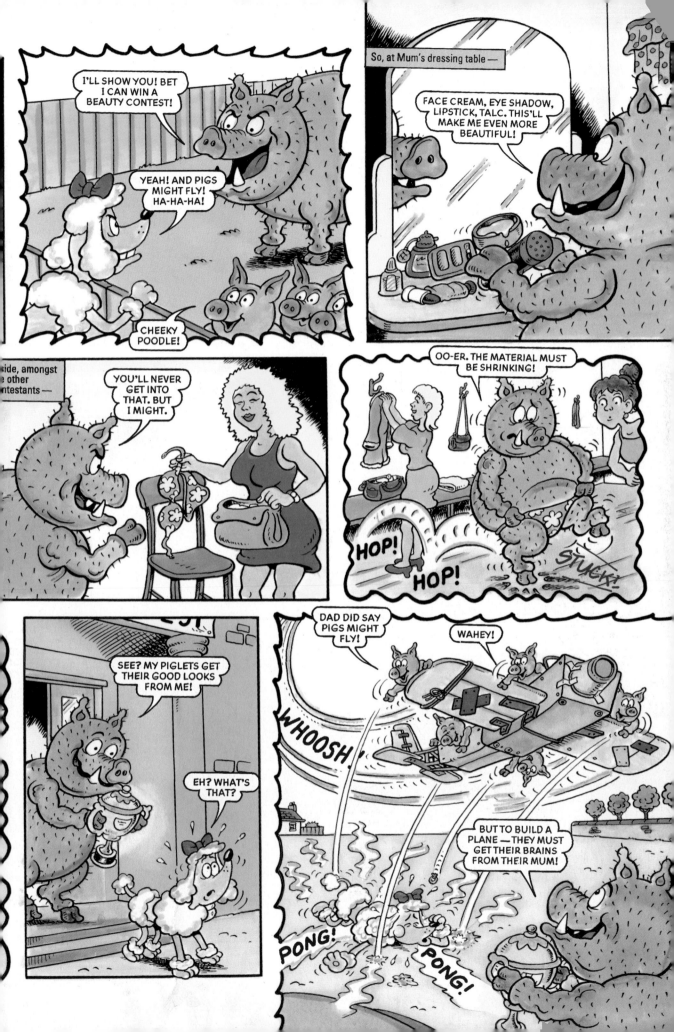

FOR WHOM THE MENACE TOOLS

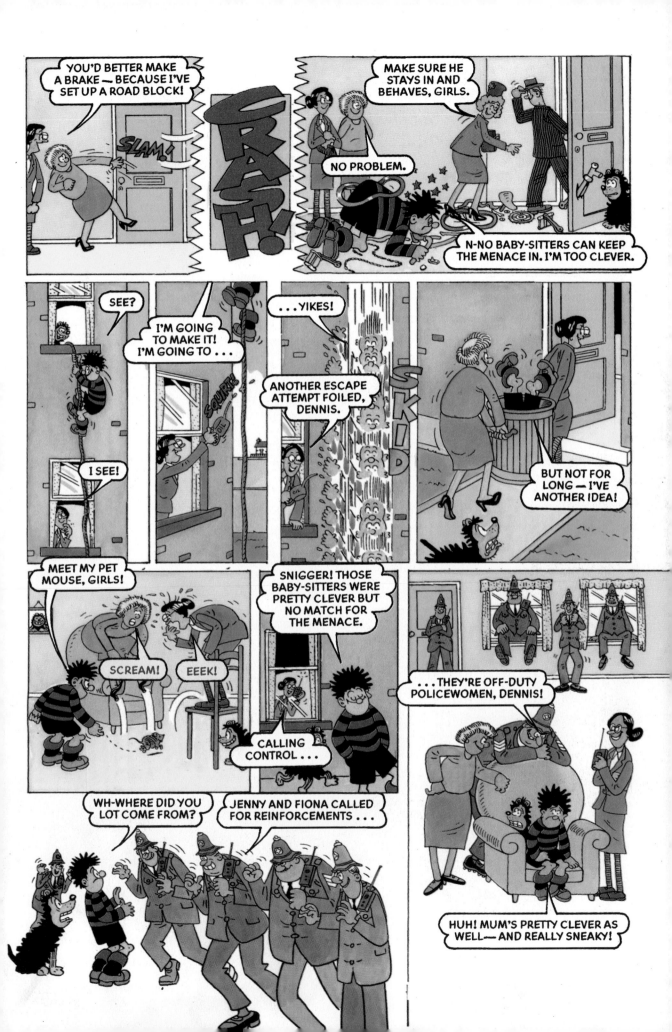

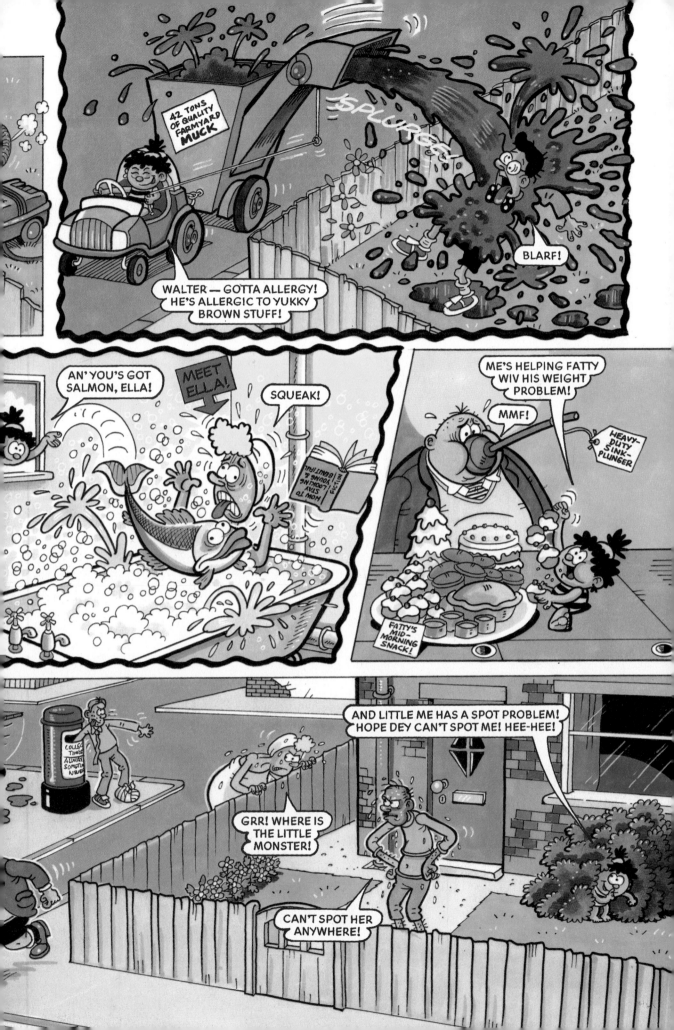

DENNIS'S FIELD DAY

Mark Timmins, Highwoods, Colchester.

Dear Dennis I want a BEANO CLUB treehouse. With a Dennis flag on it and I want to come your BEANO Club treehouse.

Love from Mark Timmins.

Jack Anderson, Dundee.

Dennis and Bea the two Menaces caught on computer. by Zoe Bradford

Zoe Bradford, Clanfield, Bampton.

Richard Curtis, Boston, Lincs.

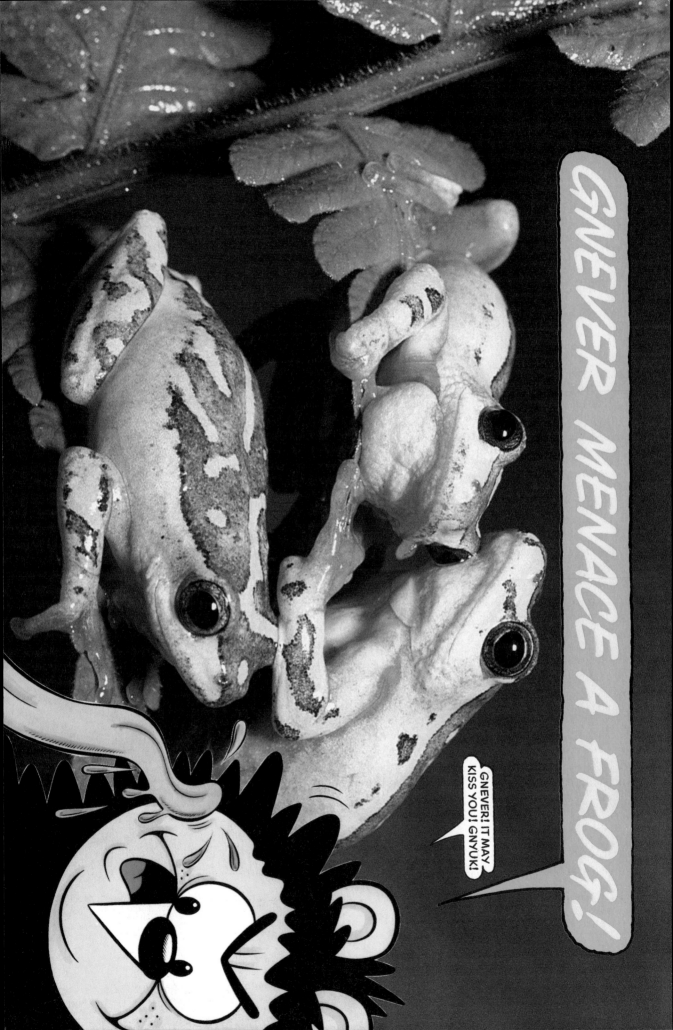

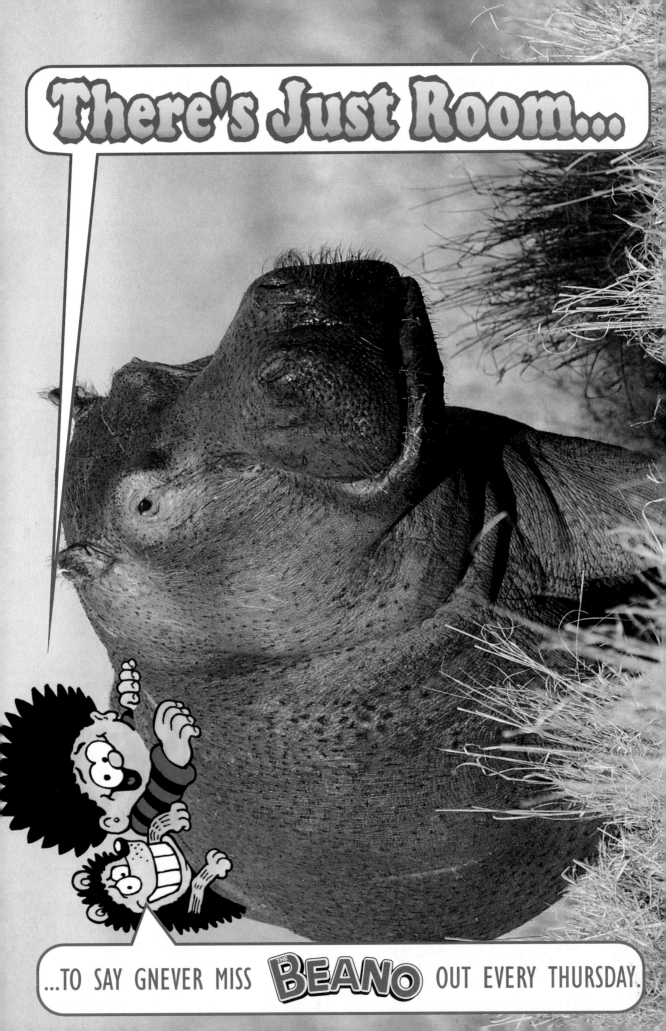